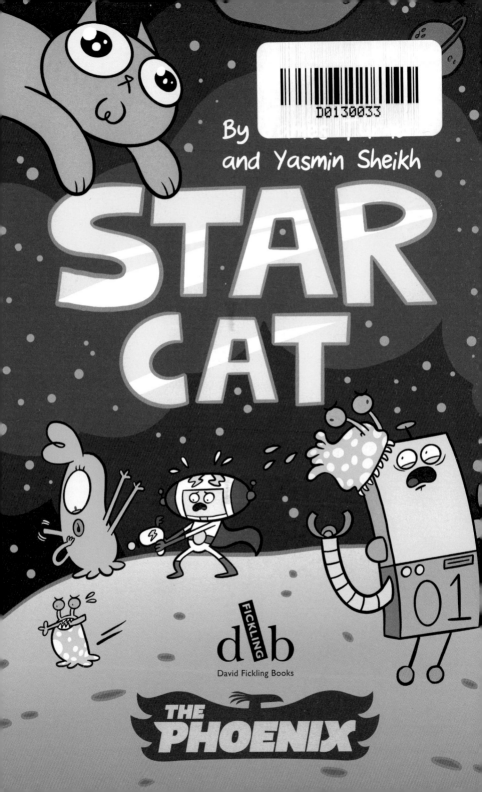

For Sara and Swinton - JT
For Robin and Sascha, my biggest hype men - YS

STAR CAT
is a
DAVID FICKLING BOOK

First published in Great Britain in 2021 by
David Fickling Books, 31 Beaumont Street, Oxford, OX1 2NP

www.davidficklingbooks.com

Text © James Turner, 2021
Illustrations © Yasmin Sheikh, 2021

978-1-78845-199-4

5 7 9 10 8 6 4

Papers used by David Fickling Books are from well-managed forests
and other responsible sources.

FSC
www.fsc.org
MIX
Paper from
responsible sources
FSC® C007785

DAVID FICKLING BOOKS Reg. No. 8340307

A CIP catalogue record for this book
is available from the British Library.

Printed in Great Britain
by Bell and Bain Ltd, Glasgow.

These comics are remastered and fully redrawn versions of comics originally published in *Star Cat: Book 01*.

CONTENTS

WELCOME ABOARD

Captain Spaceington

Captain Spaceington dreams of being the bravest ever captain, but somehow, whenever a mission comes along, things never quite go to plan.

Super-Computer

External Aural Receptor (E.A.R.)

Bridge

Bathroom

Bio-Garden

Fuel Tank

Shock Absorber

Pilot

Dipdpmbuf cjtdvjut tqsfbe xjui lfudivq. Dmjnc vq b mbeefs boe kvnq joup b txjnnjoh qppm gjmmfe xjui kbn. Nz uspvtfst ibwf uvsofe joup b qvsqmf hjsbggf. J ibwf tffo uif gvuvsf beo ju jt kvtu b sfbmmz cjh pxm.

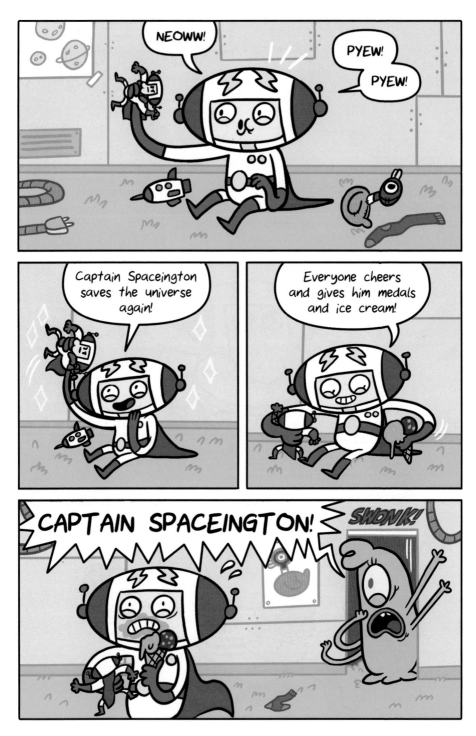

13

14

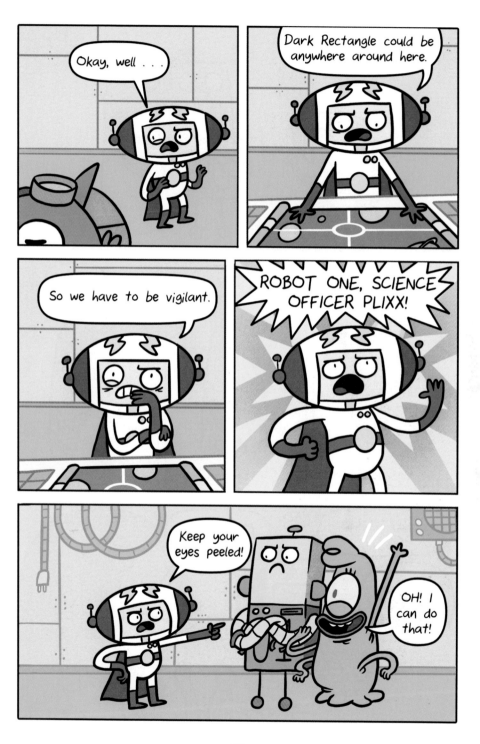

No one has set foot on this mysterious world in a thousand years.

But what is this?

On the surface are that master of polygonal peril, Dark Rectangle, and his loyal henchshape, Murky Hexagon!

What villainous scheme is afoot?!

At last, we've found it!

Ooh.

The Great Galactic Stopper!

Um, very impressive, oh perpendicular potentate. But, um, what does it do?

It's this stopper that keeps all the air in the galaxies, and when I pull it out . . .

I will deflate the universe!

WHAHAHAHAHAHAHAHAHA!

37

39

41

43

45

46

48

At Space HQ

The Space Mayor called us back urgently after our mission on Inflatia!

DOCKED: STAR CAT

BZZZT

01

That can only mean one thing . . .

OH! I KNOW!

He's holding a surprise party for his pet hamster and didn't want us to miss it!

54

55

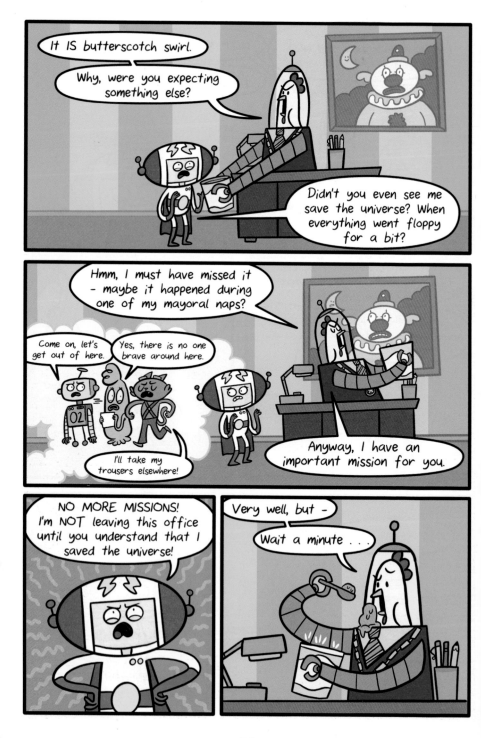

64

68

69

75

76

79

80

83

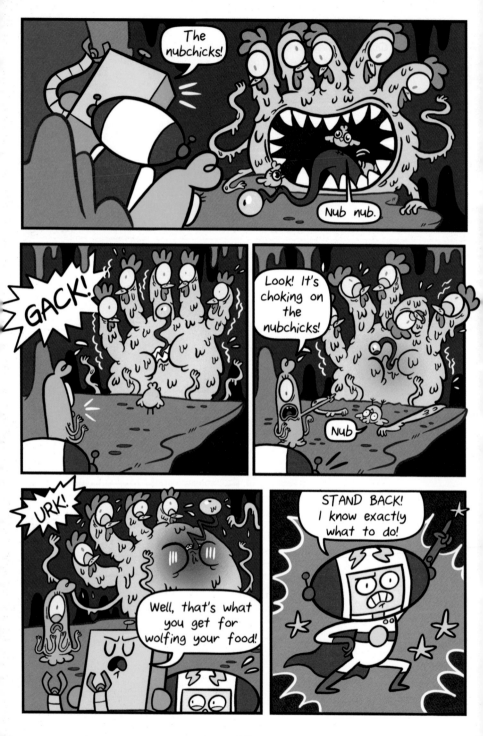

84

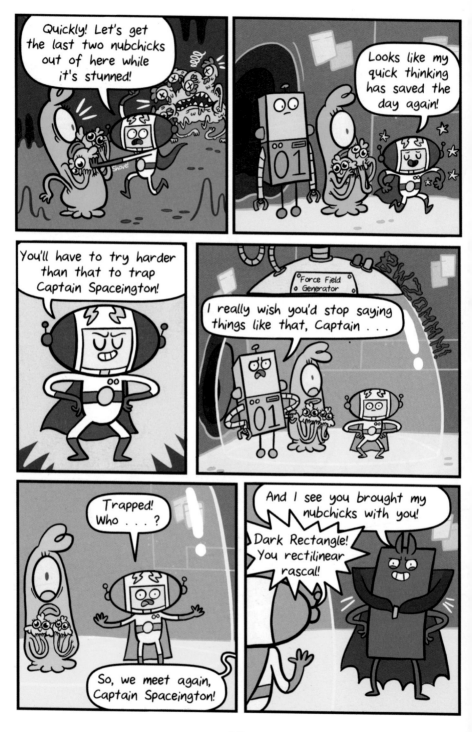

95

97

108

111

117

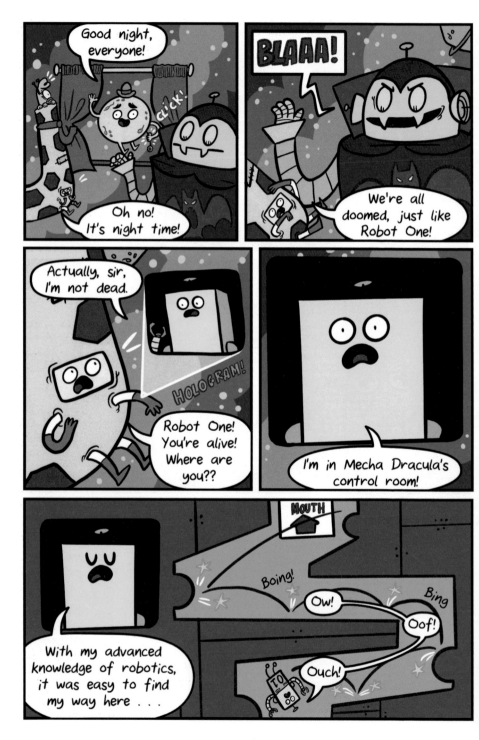

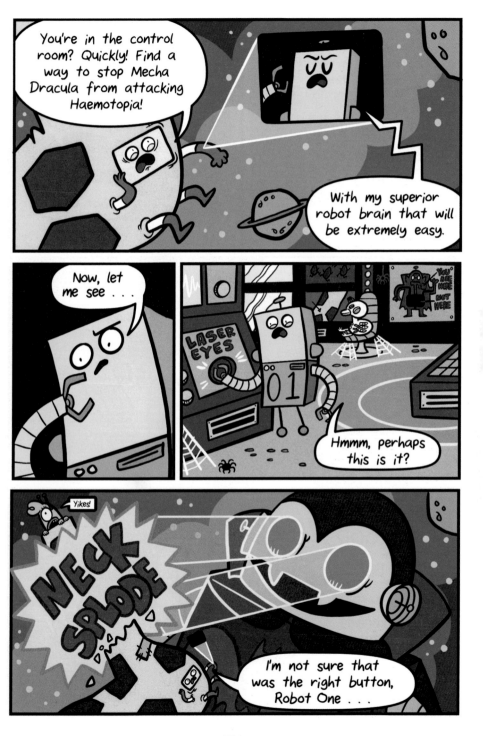

122

125

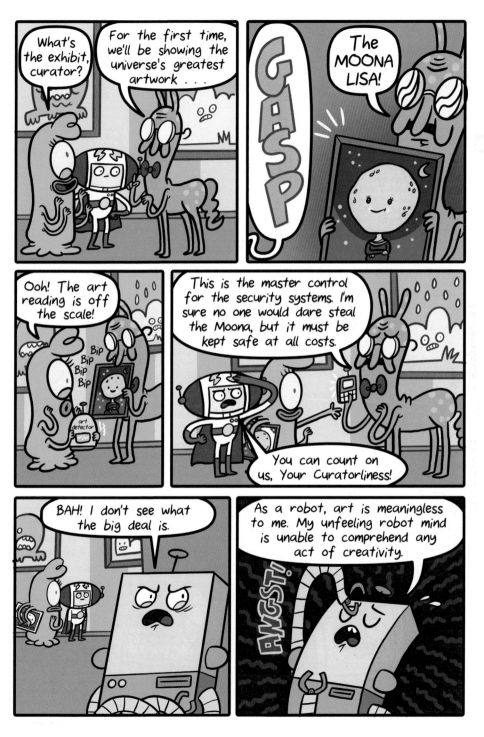

133

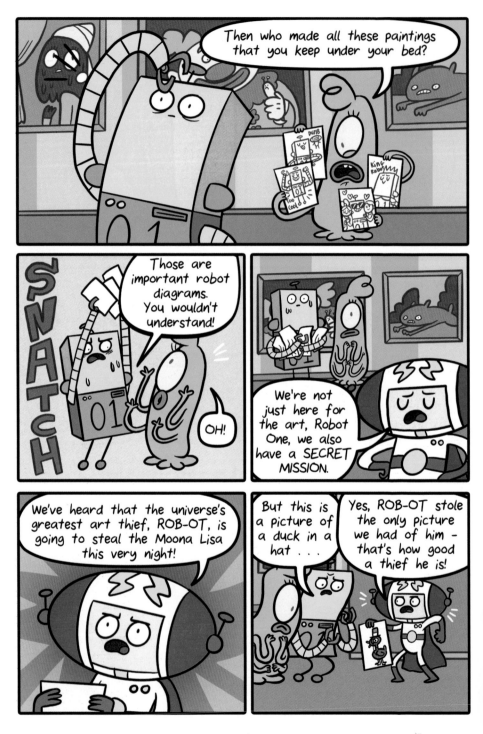

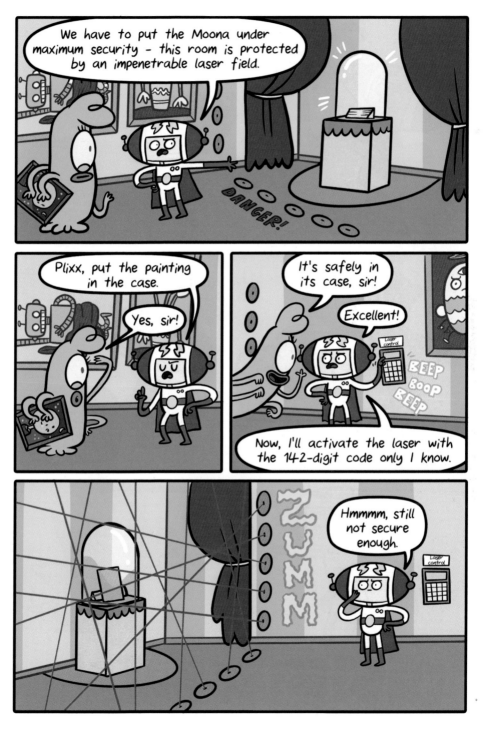

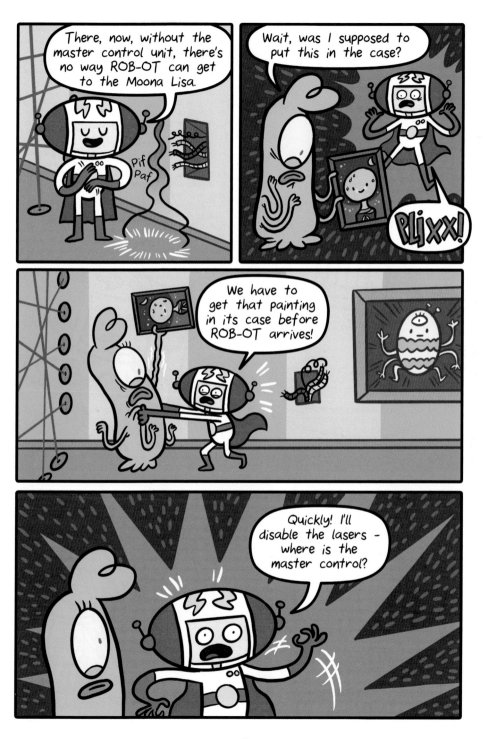

137

138

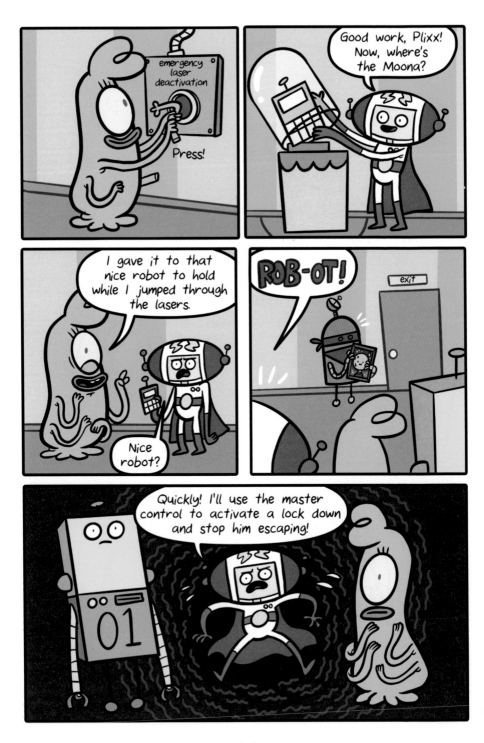

140

143

145

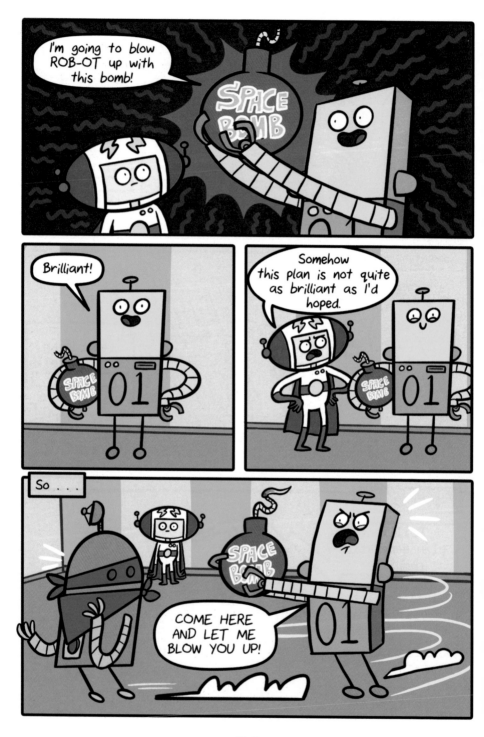

146

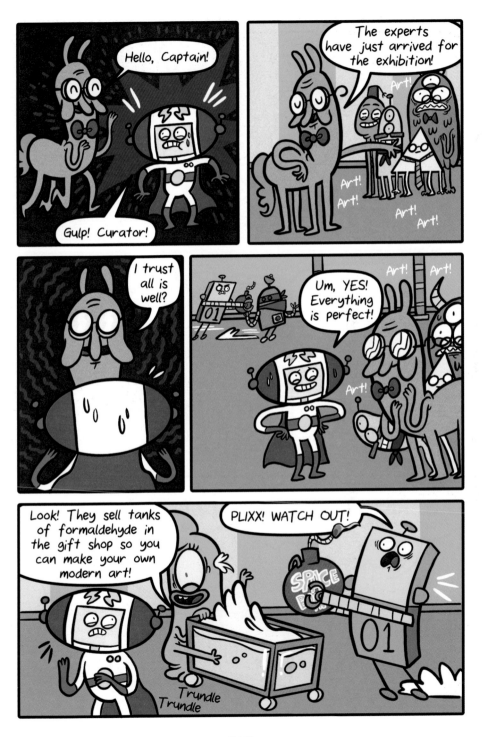

149

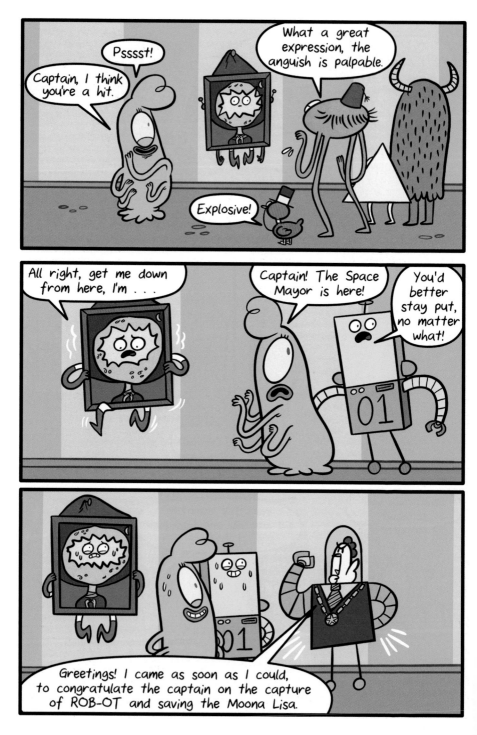

154

155

157

159

161

166

169

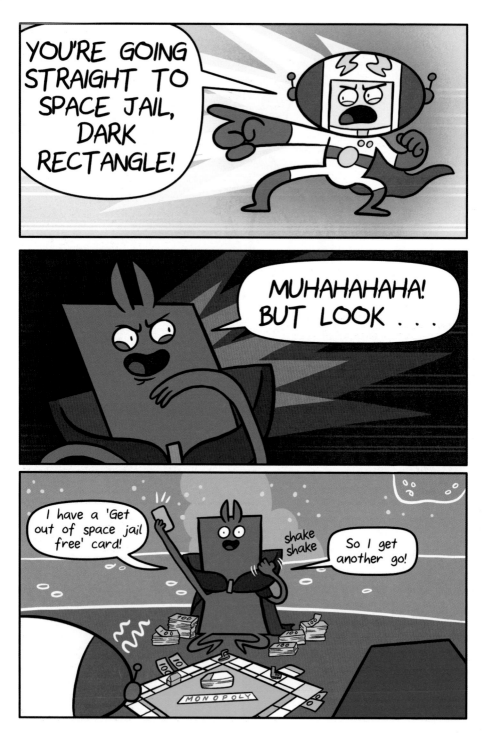

172

173

174

175

179

185

WHAT YOU'll NEED:

1 Paper, to draw on

2 A pencil, to draw with

3 Pencil sharpener to keep your pencil point pointy

4 A rubber

5 A felt-tip pen for tracing your drawing once you are happy with it

6 Optional, but recommended: A drink and a snack

HOW TO DRAW
CAPTAIN SPACEINGTON

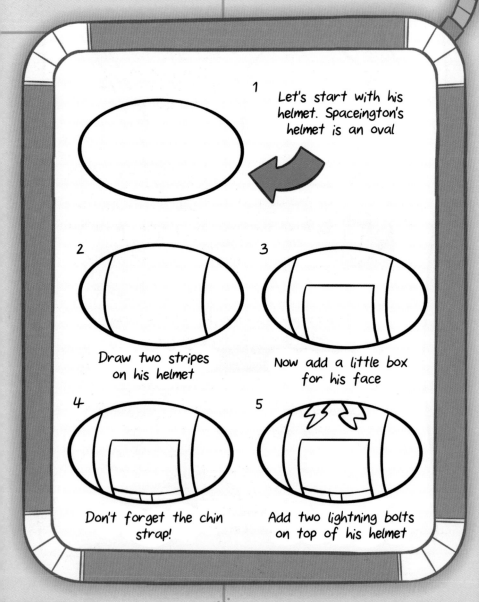

1 Let's start with his helmet. Spaceington's helmet is an oval

2 Draw two stripes on his helmet

3 Now add a little box for his face

4 Don't forget the chin strap!

5 Add two lightning bolts on top of his helmet

6

Add a half circle
to each side of
his helmet

7

Now draw two tiny
lollipops on top of
the half circles for
his antennae

8

Add two circles
with two black
dots for his
eyes. And add a
tiny stripe for
his mouth

Try practising some more expressions:

Not impressed

A bit worried

Happy and smug

9

Add a shape that looks like half a pickle for his body

10

Now add two noddle-looking arms to his body

They don't have to be straight, they can be wiggly too!

Add stripes on his arm for his glove

11

Now try adding two sticks for his legs with little feet on the end

Add stripes for his boots!

12

A cape on his back and a belt

13

Lastly, draw three circles for his belt buckle and his two mini medals

Now you've drawn Captain Spaceington! Don't worry if you didn't do it perfectly. Just keep practising and you'll get better and better!

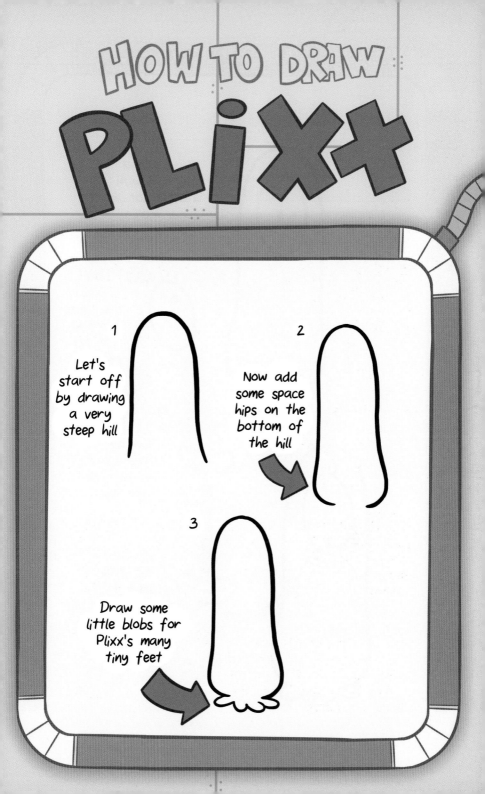

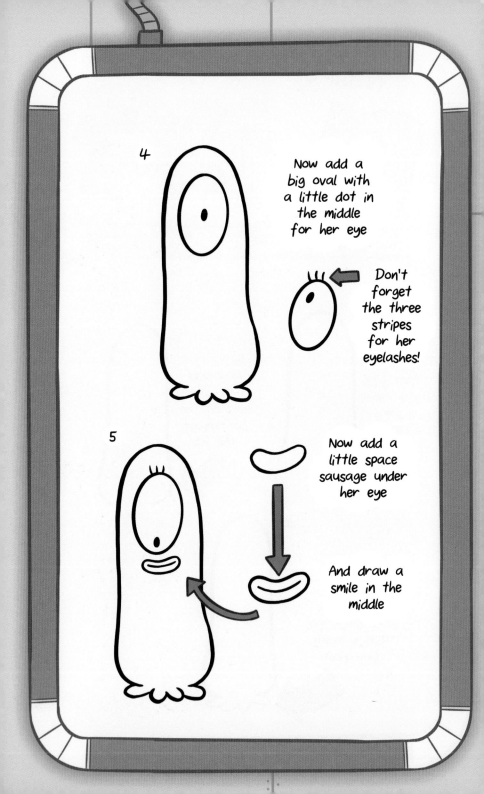

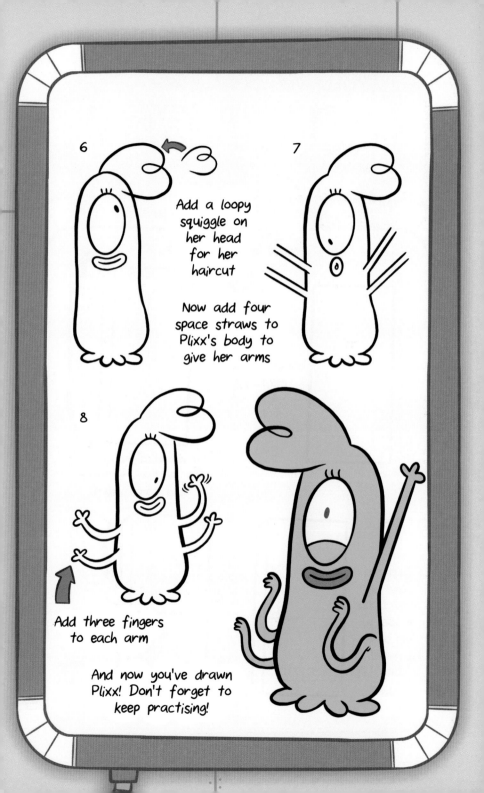

6

Add a loopy squiggle on her head for her haircut

Now add four space straws to Plixx's body to give her arms

7

8

Add three fingers to each arm

And now you've drawn Plixx! Don't forget to keep practising!

HOW TO DRAW
ROBOT ONE

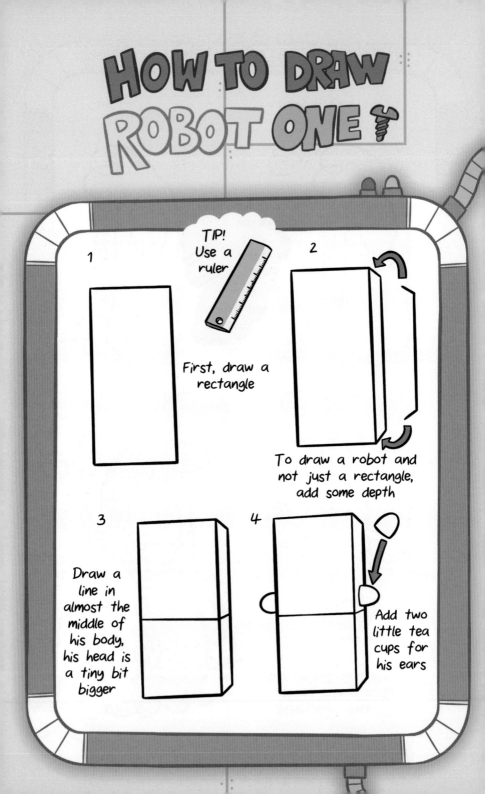

1

TIP!
Use a ruler

First, draw a rectangle

2

To draw a robot and not just a rectangle, add some depth

3

Draw a line in almost the middle of his body, his head is a tiny bit bigger

4

Add two little tea cups for his ears

5 Now give him two eyes and a mouth

You can try out some more expressions

6 Add a squished lollipop shape on top of his head. This is his antenna

7 Add two thick noodle arms on his sides and draw stripes on them

8 Now draw Robot One's robot space claw at the end of his noodle arms

A

B

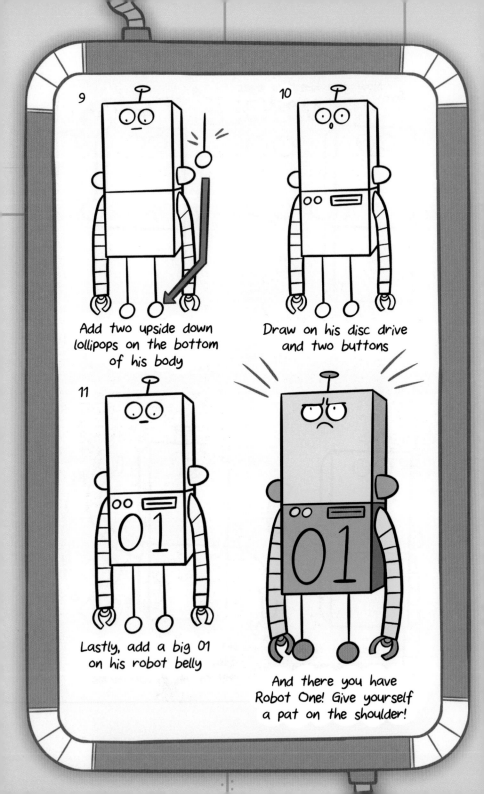

9

Add two upside down lollipops on the bottom of his body

10

Draw on his disc drive and two buttons

11

Lastly, add a big 01 on his robot belly

And there you have Robot One! Give yourself a pat on the shoulder!

THE WHOLE TEAM

Now that you've learnt to draw them all,
it's time to put the team together!

ABOUT THE AUTHORS

Born on a distant planet known as 'Earth', James Turner is a bipedal humanoid who has been making comics since the birth of time itself (around 2004). His other interests include board games, improv, and making explosion noises with his mouth.

Yasmin Sheikh is an illustrator who lives in the Netherlands, a tiny and flat country in Europe. She likes drawing comics, playing video games, cats, chocolate and cats made of chocolate, but no chocolate made of cats. That would be weird.